The New Novello Choral Edition

WOLFGANG AMADEUS M

Mass in C minor

(K.427/417a)

for two soprano, tenor and bass soloists, double SATB chorus and orchestra

Edited and reconstructed by Philip Wilby

Vocal score
Piano reduction by Michael Pilkington

Order No: NOV 078452

NOVELLO PUBLISHING LIMITED
14-15 Berners Street, LONDON, W1T 3LJ

It is requested that on all concert notices and programmes acknowledgement is made to 'The New Novello Choral Edition'.

Es wird gebeten, auf sämtlichen Konzertankündigungen und Programmen 'The New Novello Choral Edition' als Quelle zu erwähnen.

Il est exigé que toutes notices et programmes de concerts, comportent des remerciements à 'The New Novello Choral Edition'.

Orchestral material is available on hire from the Publisher.

Orchestermaterial ist beim Verlag erhältlich.

Les partitions d'orchestre sont en location disponibles chez l'editeur.

Permission to reproduce the Preface of this Edition must be obtained from the Publisher.

Die Erlaubnis, das Vorwort dieser Ausgabe oder Teile desselben zu reproduzieren, muß beim Verlag eingeholt werden.

Le droit de reproduction de ce document à partir de la préface doit être obtenu de l'éditeur.

Cover illustrations: Memorial to Wolfgang Amadeus Mozart (1756-91), engraving of 1789
Johann Georg Mansfeld (1764-1817), The Hague Municipal Museum/Bridgeman Art Library;
Portrait of Constanze Mozart (1762-1842), lithograph of 1828 (Austrian School, 18th century),
Mozart Museum, Salzburg/Bridgeman Art Library

© 2004 Novello & Company Limited

Published in Great Britain by Novello Publishing Limited
Head office: 14-15 Berners Street, LONDON, W1T 3LJ
Tel: 0207 612 7429   Fax: 020 7612 7546

Sales and Hire: Music Sales Distribution Centre
Newmarket Road, Bury St Edmunds, Suffolk, IP33 3YB
Tel +44 (0)1284 702600   Fax +44 (0)1284 768301

Web: www.musicroom.com   e-mail: music@musicsales.co.uk

Music setting by Enigma Music Production Services

CONTENTS

PREFACE

The genesis of Mozart's C minor Mass is unique. Shortly before Mozart and Constanze Weber were married in 1782, the composer undertook to write a large-scale setting of the mass. Five months later, on the 4th of January 1783, he wrote to his father from his home in Vienna:

> *I truly made this vow to myself, and I truly hope to keep it…The score of half a mass,*
> *which is lying here waiting to be finished, is the best proof that I really made the promise.*

This 'half-mass' consisted of settings of Kyrie, Gloria, Sanctus and Benedictus, and was first performed in the Abbey church of St Peter in Salzburg on the feast of St Amandus, 26 October 1783. The scale of these movements is much larger than any of his previous church music. Mozart clearly relished this opportunity to expand the horizons of his musical vision (which had been so curtailed by his former employer Archbishop Colloredo) and also to show off his new wife by composing some of his finest music for her to sing. The whole work is something of a showcase for sopranos, and is filled with fine solos, and magnificently competitive duets. Despite the fact that it is not a complete mass setting, the C minor Mass may be regarded as the first true 'Concert Mass' from the Viennese Golden Age.

The setting of just the Kyrie, Gloria, Sanctus and Benedictus may be explained by the liturgical practice of Mozart's day. It was not usual to sing the Agnus Dei at a choral mass with orchestra, nor the Credo except on Sundays and certain major festivals. Even the original trombone parts, so much a feature of the extant movements, were probably omitted on Saturdays. We may assume then, that Mozart had provided all the material required at the mass's first performance. On his return to Vienna, Mozart did sketch out settings of the Credo in unum Deum and Et incarnatus est, and make a very brief sketch of part of the Agnus Dei; ultimately, there was no real incentive for him to fulfil his vow.

Our intentions in this edition are threefold: to provide a complete score of Mozart's surviving music (including unpicking the Sanctus and Benedictus which exist only in a short score by a third party); to construct the missing movements from existing material in order to extend Mozart's half-mass into a conventional six-movement mass setting and to provide an approximation of the original liturgical context.

In the course of constructing the missing parts of the Mass we have drawn on a number of sources: a sketch titled 'Solfegio' [sic] (KV 393) that Mozart had already used in the composition of the 'Christe eleison', sketch material for the 'Credo in unum Deum' and 'Et incarnatus est',some material from the Attwood Studybook and movements from the Viennese oratorio *Davidde penitente* (K 469). *Davidde penitente*, completed by March 1785, recycles all the music from the 'Kyrie' and 'Gloria' of the C minor Mass alongside newly composed material, some of which we have used in this reconstruction. The musical provenance of each movement is detailed below.

Kyrie
All the music here is original Mozart.

Gloria.
All the music here is original Mozart.

Credo
Credo in unum Deum
The existing material for this movement consists of all the voice parts and partially complete orchestration. The missing trumpet, trombone and timpani parts have been reconstructed.

Et incarnatus est
The existing material for this movement consists of a complete voice part and a partially complete orchestration. Missing string parts have been reconstructed. The manuscript contains two blank staves that we presume were left for horns to complete the wind ensemble. These parts have been added.

Crucifixus / Et resurrexit

The music for this section of the Credo is taken from the soprano aria 'Tra l'oscure ombre funeste' from *Davidde penitente*, and is recast for chorus.

Et in Spiritum Sanctum

The music for this section of the Credo is taken from the tenor aria 'A te, fra tanti affanni' from *Davidde penitente*, and is recast for four soloists.

Et unam, sanctam

This section draws on fugal material from the Attwood Sketchbook, which is freely adapted and expanded.

Sanctus / Benedictus

The source for these movements is an incomplete short score in Peter Fischer's manuscript. Only Mozart's brass and wind parts survive. This has been unpicked.

Agnus Dei

This reuses the 'Solfegio' sketch already used by Mozart in the 'Christe eleison'; a contrapuntal working in the margin of an unrelated sheet (using the text 'Dona nobis pacem'), and the final movement of *Davidde penitente*. The use of this movement effects a reprise of the Cum sancto spiritu, with the addition of a vocal cadenza unique to *Davidde penitente*.

★

The reconstruction into a conventional six-movement mass results in a large work suitable for concert performances. This reconstruction, however, will not satisfy those who wish to perform Mozart's work in a liturgical or quasi-liturgical setting, nor does it help contextualise the work.

These issues are discussed in full in the Appendix (p.175) that also includes the Plainchant Propers for the Mass for a Bishop, (using the 1871 Pustet reprint of the 1614/15 originals). Whilst there is no suggestion that eighteenth-century chant would have been sung alongside Mozart's music, nevertheless in St Peter's Abbey, the monks continued to sing the chant throughout the century, and it is clear that Mozart was familiar with much of the chant repertoire as echoes and quotations are to be found in his work. It is clear that when the liturgy was celebrated with an orchestral mass, all the music would have been provided by the professional musicians, (including perhaps an Epistle Sonata, a communion motet, and one of the many Offertoria by such composers as Michael Haydn, or by Mozart himself). A contemporary liturgical performance could then, quite plausibly, include the chant pieces (sung by a different group) both to complete the liturgical provision and as a reminder of the whole context within which Mozart was working.

Philip Wilby
Fr Peter Allan

MASS IN C MINOR

WOLFGANG AMADEUS MOZART

KYRIE

GLORIA
GLORIA IN EXCELSIS DEO

-cel - - - - - - - - - sis De - o. Glo - -
glo - - - - - - ri - a in ex - cel - sis, glo -
glo - - - - - - ri - a in ex - cel - sis,
in ex - cel -
- - - ri - a in ex - cel - sis, glo - ri - a in ex - cel - sis, in ex - cel - sis, in ex-
- - - ri - a in ex - cel - sis, glo - ri - a in ex - cel - sis, in ex-
glo - ri - a in ex - cel - sis, in ex - cel - sis, in ex - cel - sis, in ex-
- - - - - sis De - o. Glo - ri - a in ex-
- cel - sis, in ex - cel - - - - - - - sis De - - - - -
- cel - sis, in ex - cel - - - - - sis, in ex - cel -
- cel - - - - - - sis, in ex - cel -
- cel - sis, in ex - cel - sis, in ex - cel - - - - - - sis, in ex-

LAUDAMUS TE

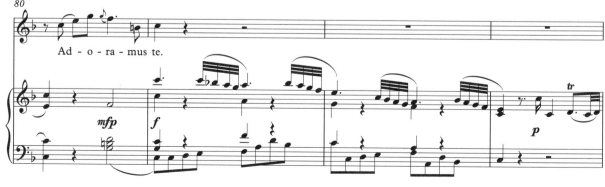

GRATIAS

DOMINE DEUS

QUI TOLLIS

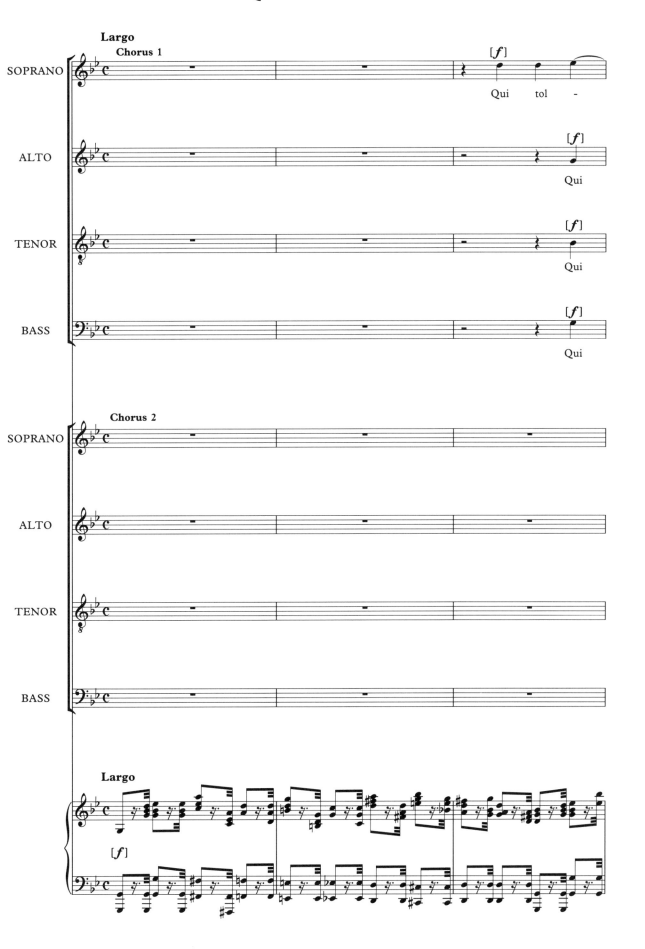

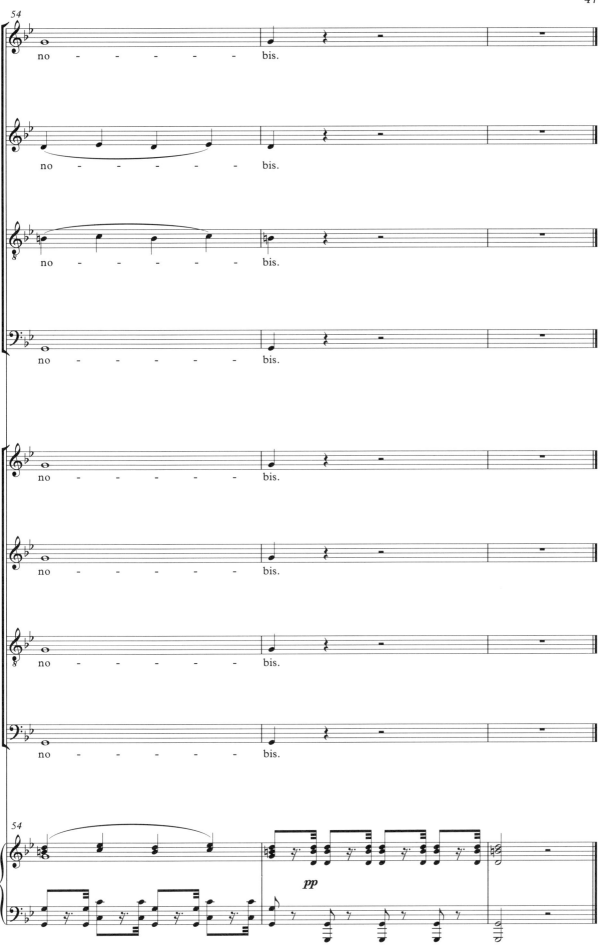

QUONIAM

52

JESU CHRISTE

CUM SANCTO SPIRITU

97
- - men, a - - - - - - - - - - men,
- - - - - - - - cto Spi - ri - tu, in glo -
- men, a - - - - - - - - - -
a - - - - - - - - - - - - - -
97
102
a - - - - - men, a - - - - - - men.
- - - ri-a De-i Pa - - - - - - - tris.
- - - - - - - - - - - - men, a - - - - -
- - - - - - - - - - - men. Cum San - -
D
102
D
107
Cum San - - - - - - - - cto
- - - - - - - - - - - - - - - -
- - - - - - cto Spi - ri - tu. A -
107

CREDO
CREDO IN UNUM DEUM

ET INCARNATUS EST

et ho - mo fac - tus est, fac — — — — — — tus

est, fac — — — — —

- - - - - - - tus est,

G Cadenza

fac — — — — — — — —

- - - - - - - - -

- tus est.

CRUCIFIXUS

ET RESURREXIT

ET IN SPIRITUM SANCTUM

100

ET UNAM, SANCTAM

SANCTUS

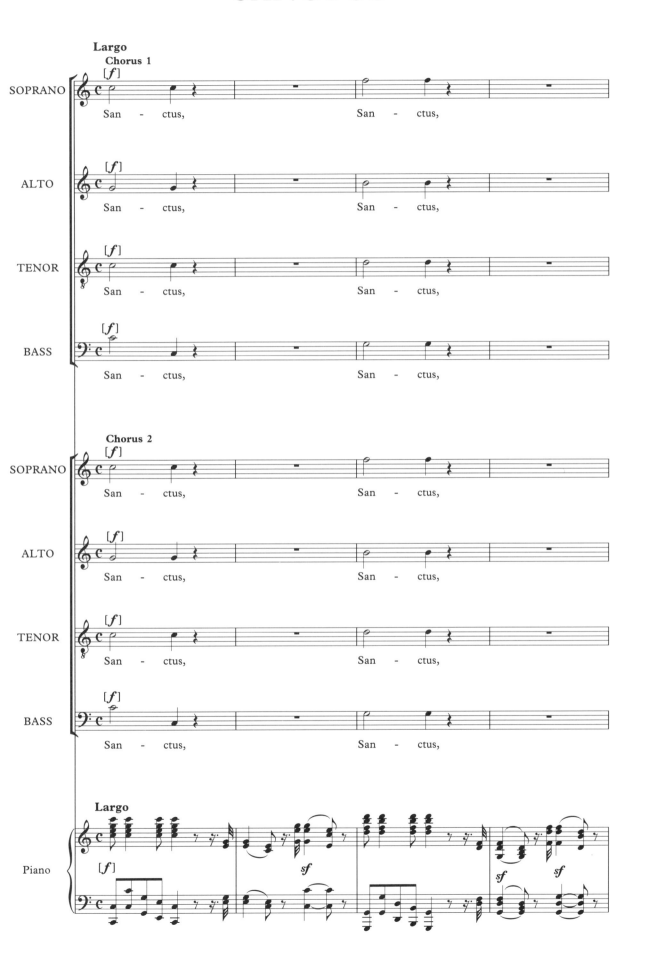

20
sis, in ex - cel - sis. Ho - san - na
na in ex - cel - sis. Ho - san - na, ho - san - na, ho - san - na
In ex - cel
sis. Ho - san - na in ex - cel - sis. Ho - san
na, in ex - cel - sis, ex - cel - sis,
20

BENEDICTUS

AGNUS DEI

152

181
Do - - - - na no - - - bis
no - - - bis pa - cem, pa - - -
185
cem.
Do - - - na
pa - cem, pa - - - cem.
- cem. Do-na no - - bis pa - - - - - - -
189
Do - - - na no - - - bis
no - - - bis pa - cem, pa - - -

APPENDIX

Mozart and the Liturgy

Many will welcome this edition of the Mass in C minor as an addition to the concert repertoire. There will also be those, however, who wish to use the setting of the mass at a celebration of the Eucharist. The first performance was, we know, at the mass in St Peter's Abbey Salzburg on the feast of St Amandus, but contemporary liturgical use invites new considerations. Since the liturgical renewal in the Western church that has its roots in the nineteenth century and achieved some degree of consensus in the decades following the second Vatican Council, there are some commonly shared expectations in terms of key "moments" in the liturgy that are very different from those of the late eighteenth century. With this in mind, we include this Appendix as an aid to the construction of effective liturgy.

The first simple possibility is to use only the movements of the Mass that Mozart completed for the first performance: Kyrie, Gloria and Sanctus, with the Benedictus performed separately during Communion. This is close to the actual practice of the second half of the eighteenth century in Austria and Southern Germany: on weekdays that were not solemnities, the Creed would not have been used; the Agnus Dei was not commonly sung; and the Benedictus would have been sung after the Great Elevation at the culmination of the Canon.

Some may wish to contemplate singing the reconstructed Mass in its entirety. This is more difficult to justify. It cannot be argued on the grounds of historical reconstruction since the only known liturgical performance was its first. To suggest that this is what would have happened had Mozart completed the score is also doubtful: even with a complete score, the Creed would only have been sung on a Sunday or solemnity and even then the Agnus Dei would normally have been omitted. In our own time the case is harder to sustain because of the great length of the score. To sing the complete Mass would seriously distort and unbalance the liturgical action.

A third possibility is to sing the Kyrie, Gloria, Sanctus and Benedictus as indicated above but to include the chant propers for the Common of a Bishop. This is, once again, not in order to realise an historical reconstruction, but to contextualise Mozart's music and make some exploration of the world of eighteenth-century liturgy in a contemporary dimension. The chant continued to be sung in monastic communities through the eighteenth century and it was in the Benedictine Abbey Church of St Peter that this Mass was first heard. Its influence is evident in the work of composers of the period, not least Mozart. Records of the time leave little doubt but that the monastic schola would not have sung the chant propers at an orchestral mass, although they did so at other sung masses. We have thus included the Introit, Gradual, Alleluia, Offertory and Communion in the edition of the chant that followed the reforms of the Council of Trent (a simplified and less elegant form certainly) as one possibility for a contemporary liturgical celebration. It should be noted that the chant would have been performed more slowly and deliberately (though not precisely metrically) than contemporary practice.

It is our hope that this appendix may stimulate reflection on the appropriate liturgical use of much of the classical repertoire and enhance the understanding of those who wish to know this particular Mass and its context better.

Peter Allan CR

PROPERS FOR THE COMMON OF A BISHOP

These Propers are taken from the edition of the Roman Gradual published in Regensburg in 1871 by Pustet, reproducing the reforms of Pope Paul V and thus the chants that were in use in Salzburg throughout the eighteenth century. Two versions are given, the first in neumatic notation, the second in more conventional five-line stave notation, for those who are unfamiliar with neumatic notation. The asterisk indicates the intonation for each piece that is normally sung by a solo cantor, the other voices entering together after the intonation. In the Introit, the antiphon *Statuit ei Dominus* is sung first; cantors then sing the psalm verse (indicated by *Ps.* and taken here from Psalm 132); and all repeat the antiphon. The Alleluia is intoned by the cantor up to the quarter bar; all then sing the whole alleluia from the beginning. The verse follows (sung by cantors) and the alleluia is repeated once. In the Gradual ℣. indicates the verse that is sung by a solo voice or small group.

INTROIT

Mode 1

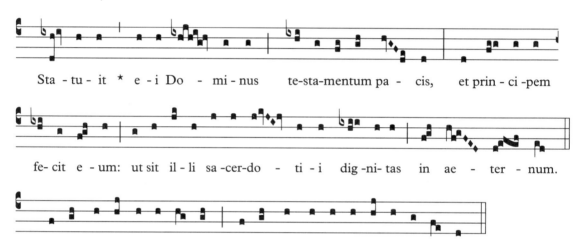

Sta - tu - it * e - i Do - mi - nus te-sta-mentum pa - cis, et prin - ci -pem

fe- cit e - um: ut sit il - li sa -cer-do - ti - i dig -ni- tas in ae - ter - num.

Ps. Me-men-to Do-mi- ne Da - vid: et o-mnis mansu - e - tu-di- nis e - jus.

GRADUAL

Mode V

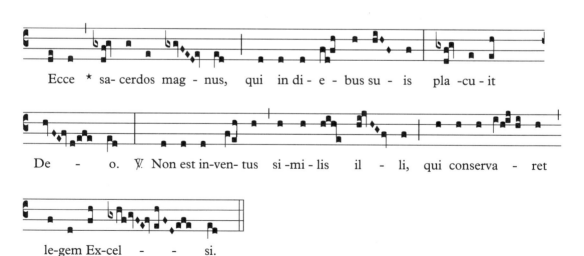

Ecce * sa- cerdos mag - nus, qui in di - e - bus su - is pla -cu - it

De - o. ℣. Non est in-ven- tus si -mi - lis il - li, qui conserva - ret

le-gem Ex-cel - - si.

ALLELUIA

Mode II

Al - le - lu - ia.

Hic est sa -cer - dos, quem co-ro- na- vit Do - mi -nus.

OFFERTORY

Mode VII

Inve - ni ⋆ Da - vid servum me - um, o - le- o san-cto me - o unxi e - um:

ma-nus e - nim me - a auxi- li - a - bi - tur e - - i, et bra - chi - um

me - um con-for-ta - bit e - um.

COMMUNION

Mode VII

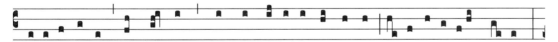

Fi-de-lis servus, ⋆ et pru - dens, quem consti -tu- it do-mi- nus su-per fami- li-am su - am:

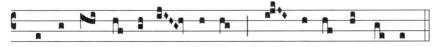

ut det il - lis in tem - po -re tri - ti - ci men-su - ram.

In this second version the pitch is only indicative: the pieces should be sung at a pitch that is convenient for the voices and consonant with the music that precedes and follows. Rhythm derives primarily from the text, although by the late eighteenth century some more mannered, near-metrical traits had crept in to performance of the chant. White notes suggest definite lengthenings, but should not be understood as twice as long as black notes.

INTROIT

Mode 1

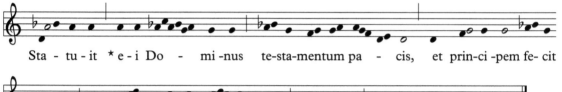

Sta - tu - it * e - i Do - mi - nus te-sta-mentum pa - cis, et prin-ci -pem fe- cit

e - um: ut sit il - li sa -cer-do - ti - i dig - ni - tas in ae - ter - num.

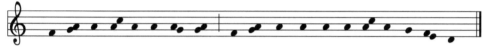

Ps Memen-to Do-mi- ne Da - vid: et o-mnis mansu - e -tu-di - nis e - jus.

GRADUAL

Mode V

Ec-ce * sa - cerdos mag - nus, qui in di - e - bus su - is pla - cu - it

De - o. ℣. Non est inven - tus si-mi -lis il - li, qui conserva - ret

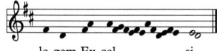

le-gem Ex-cel - - si.

ALLELUIA

Mode II

Al -le - lu - ia.

Hic est sa-cer - dos, quem co-ro-na-vit Do - mi -nus.

OFFERTORY

Mode VIII

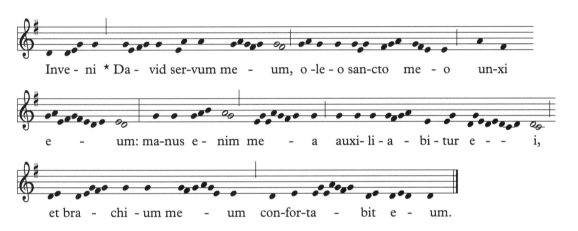

Inve - ni ⋆ Da - vid ser-vum me - um, o -le - o san-cto me - o un-xi

e - um: ma-nus e - nim me - a auxi-li-a - bi-tur e - - i,

et bra - chi - um me - um con-for-ta - bit e - um.

COMMUNION

Mode VII

Fide-lis servus, ⋆ et pru - dens, quem consti - tu - it do-minus su - per fami-li - am

su - am: ut det il - lis in tem - po-re tri - ti - ci men-su - ram.

NOVELLO REVISED STANDARD CHORAL EDITIONS

Fully revised and edited performing versions of many of the major works in the large-scale choral concert repertoire, replacing the standard Novello editions, often putting back the composers' intentions, restoring the original text, modernised accompaniments and providing new English translations. **Orchestral material, where necessary, is available on hire.**

J.S. BACH
(ed. Neil Jenkins)
Ascension Oratorio
NOV090860
German and English text
Christmas Oratorio
NOV072500
German and English text
Easter Oratorio
NOV090849
German and English text
Magnificat in D and E♭
NOV072529
German and English text in the
four Lauds in the E♭ version
Mass in B minor
NOV078430
St. John Passion
NOV072489
German and English text
St. Matthew Passion
NOV072478
German and English text

BEETHOVEN
(ed. Michael Pilkington)
**Choral Finale
to the Ninth Symphony**
NOV072490
German and English text
Mass in C NOV078560
Missa Solemnis (Mass in D)
NOV072497

BRAHMS
(ed. Pilkington)
A German Requiem
NOV072492
German and English text

DVOŘÁK
(Pilkington)
Mass in D NOV072491
Requiem NOV072516
Stabat Mater NOV072503
Te Deum NOV078573

ELGAR
(ed. Bruce Wood)
The Dream of Gerontius
NOV072530
Great is the Lord
NOV320067
Te Deum and Benedictus
NOV320078

GOUNOD
(Pilkington)
**Messe solennelle de
Sainte Cécile** NOV072495

HANDEL
Alexander's Feast
(ed. Donald Burrows)
NOV070446
Belshazzar
(Burrows) NOV070530
Dixit Dominus
(ed. Watkins Shaw)
NOV072323
Four Coronation Anthems
NOV072507
  The King Shall Rejoice
  (ed. Damian Cranmer)
  Let Thy Hand be Strengthened
  (Burrows)
  My Heart is Inditing
  (Burrows)
  Zadok the Priest
  (Burrows)
Judas Maccabaeus
(ed. Merlin Channon)
NOV072486
The King Shall Rejoice
(Cranmer) NOV072496
**Let Thy Hand be
Strengthened** *(Burrows)*
NOV072509
Messiah *(Shaw)* NOV070137
  Study Score NOV090074
My Heart is Inditing
(Burrows)
NOV072508
**O Praise the Lord (from
Chandos Anthem No. 9)**
(ed. Graydon Beeks) NOV072511
Samson (complete) *(Burrows)*
NOV090926
Full score NOV078903
This is the Day *(Burrows)*
NOV072510
Zadok the Priest *(Burrows)*
NOV290704

HAYDN
(Pilkington)
The Creation NOV072485
German and English text
The Seasons NOV072493
German and English text
Te Deum Laudamus
NOV078463
"Maria Theresa" Mass
NOV078474
Mass "In Time of War"
NOV072514
"Nelson" Mass NOV072513
"Wind Band" Mass
(Harmoniemesse) NOV078507

MAUNDER
Olivet to Calvary
NOV072487

MENDELSSOHN
(Pilkington)
Elijah NOV070201
German and English text
Hymn of Praise
NOV072506

MOZART
Requiem
(ed. Duncan Druce) NOV070529
**Coronation Mass
(Mass in C K.317)**
(Pilkington) NOV072505
Mass in C minor
(reconstr. Philip Wilby)
NOV078452

ROSSINI
Petite messe solennelle
NOV072436

SCHUBERT
**Mass in G, D.167
(SSA version)**
NOV070258

SCHÜTZ
(Jenkins)
Christmas Story
NOV072525
German and English text

STAINER
(Pilkington)
The Crucifixion
NOV072488

VERDI
(Pilkington)
Requiem
NOV072403

VIVALDI
(ed. Jasmin Cameron)
Gloria
NOV078441